The elephant that forgot

Written and illustrated
by
Shoo Rayner

We all know that elephants never
forget. Well, this is a story about
a little elephant that forgot
everything she was told.
The elephant was called Ellie.

One day Ellie's mum said to her,
'I want you to go and find your dad
and tell him to come home for tea.'
Ellie was pleased to have a job to do
so off she went to find her dad.

'Don't forget to tell your dad to come home for tea,' Ellie's mum called after her.
'I won't forget,' shouted Ellie as she walked off through the forest.

Soon Ellie met her friend, Mandy
the monkey.
'Have you seen my dad?' asked Ellie.
'Yes,' said Mandy. 'I saw him
going to the lake.'
'I've got something to tell my dad
and I must not forget it,' said Ellie.

'When I don't want to forget something
I tie a knot in my tail,' said Mandy.
'Then I can't forget.'
Mandy helped Ellie to tie a knot in
her tail, but Ellie was so big that she
couldn't see the knot.

'I know,' said Mandy. 'Tie a knot
in your trunk. Then you won't forget.'
So Mandy helped Ellie to tie a knot
in her trunk. Ellie was happy.
'Thank you, Mandy,' she said.
'Now I won't forget.'

Ellie walked off to find her dad.
Next she met her friend, Rocky
the rhinoceros.
'Have you seen my dad?' asked Ellie.
'Yes,' said Rocky. 'I saw him
by the lake.'
'I've got something to tell my dad
and I must not forget it,' said Ellie.

'When I don't want to forget something I put a pineapple on the end of my horn,' said Rocky. 'Then I can't forget.' Rocky showed Ellie how he put a pineapple on the end of his horn.

'I know,' said Rocky. 'You should put
pineapples on the ends of your tusks.
Then you won't forget.'
So Rocky helped Ellie to put
pineapples on the ends of her tusks.
Ellie was very happy.
'Thank you, Rocky,' she said.
'Now I won't forget.'

Ellie walked off to find her dad.
She was very pleased with the knot
in her trunk and the pineapples on
the ends of her tusks.
'Now I won't forget,' Ellie said.

Just then Ellie came to the lake.
She saw her dad and ran over to him.
'Hello,' said Ellie's dad. 'Why have
you got a knot in your trunk and
pineapples on your tusks? You look
very silly.'

'I've got a knot in my trunk and
   pineapples on my tusks so I won't
   forget to tell you what Mum said.'
'Well,' said Dad, 'what did Mum say?'
'Um,' said Ellie. 'Um ... Um ... Um ...'

So Dad said, 'I think we should
go home and find out what Mum said.'

Ellie took the knot out of her trunk
and took the pineapples off her tusks.
Then she followed her dad back
through the forest.

Ellie's mum smiled when she saw
them coming.
'Very good, Ellie,' she said.
'You didn't forget to tell your dad
to come home for tea.'

Ellie looked at Dad.
Dad looked at Ellie.
They began to laugh.

Then Ellie's mum
began to laugh too.
'Ellie,' she said, 'why have you got
a knot in your tail? You do look silly!'